SCIENCE ENQUIRY GAMES

Active ways to learn and revise science enquiry skills

by Anne Goldsworthy

with

Bob Ponchaud

Millgate House Education

ED CON

Educational Consultants Limited

Millgate House Education Ltd, Millgate House,
30 Mill Hill Lane, Sandbach, Cheshire, CW11 4PN, UK.
www.millgatehouse.co.uk

in collaboration with EDCON, Educational Consultants Ltd,
15 Rosehill Park, Emmer Green, Reading, Berkshire, RG4 8XE, UK.

First published in Great Britain by Millgate House Publishers, 2007.
Reprinted 2008.

© Edcon

British Library Cataloguing in Publication Data
A record for this book is available from the British Library.

ISBN 9780-95275067-3

EAN 9780952750673

Typesetting, Graphic Design and PDF by Kathryn Stawpert
Illustrations by Ged Mitchell.
Edited by Brenda Keogh and Stuart Naylor

Printed and bound in Great Britain by Crewe Colour Printers

Acknowledgments

There are several groups of people who have had an impact on this publication through their willingness to trial, and provide feedback on, our ideas and resources.

Claire Holt and schools in Bradford who gave us invaluable help when developing the games.

The teachers in Cheshire who provided critical comments on the book.

Kathryn Stawpert who has expertly drawn all the materials together and turned them into a fun resource book and PDF.

Melissa Wood who provided the inspiration for the cover design.

Ged Mitchell who has skilfully turned ideas into images.

Lauren Barnes who has patiently managed the illustration process.

Finally the many teachers who, during INSET sessions, let caution to the wind and joined in enthusiastically with the games. We hope they, and their children, enjoy using the resources in our book.

Introduction

ENQUIRY AND GAMES

Helping children to understand the nature of evidence is probably the most important thing we do in primary science education. We know that by equipping them with the tools of scientific enquiry, we can really help children throughout school and in everyday life. We know that children who are able to use these skills effectively, become competent and confident investigators. Scientific enquiry skills are vital to children's progress in science. This is reflected by the emphasis given to them in the end of Key Stage 2 science tests in England.

We also know how much children learn when they play games. The excitement of a game keeps them interested and motivated, and learning occurs almost without children realising that it is happening.

> 66 Helping children to understand the nature of evidence is probably the most important thing we do in primary science education. 99

However, although there are several ideas for teaching the content of science through games such as Science Ideas Bingo or Key Word Chase, there are few games to teach children about the skills of scientific enquiry. This book aims to fill that gap with a series of creative and stimulating scientific enquiry games.

BUILDING TALK INTO THE GAMES

Children talk much more readily about the content of science than the skills. At the end of an investigation, they are much more likely to tell you what they found out than how they got their evidence. Research by Robin Alexander (*Towards dialogic teaching, Re-thinking Classroom Talk*. Dialogos. 2006) highlights just how important it is to get children talking to each other in an informal way. If we want children to make progress in scientific skills then we must let them discuss the use and the purpose of skills with each other. All the games have opportunities for children to talk about the skills of science. If you never thought you'd see a group of children animatedly discussing the variables involved in fair test investigations, try playing the Fair Test Scramble. You will be amazed!

DIFFERENT WAYS TO PLAY THE GAMES

Because classrooms work in different ways, for most of the games we have provided more than one version. If it is difficult for children to move around in your classroom, fear not. The games can also be played on table-tops and the CD used on a whiteboard. There are also some paper activities related to the skills where appropriate. Use these before the game to introduce ideas or after the game to help children recognise for themselves what they have learnt.

RESOURCES

Each game comes with all the resources that you need to play it. They are also available as PDF versions on the enclosed CD. One or two additional resources are also included. The CD allows you to show resources to the whole class, make use of the interactive whiteboard tools, and print copies direct from the CD.

All you need to do now is get playing and enjoy watching your children learn scientific enquiry skills.

NB VARIABLES VS FACTORS

Throughout this book we refer to 'variables' rather than 'factors'. If your children are more used to the word 'factor' you may need to discuss this with them.

List of Games

Planning

Planning Posers

Planning

Planning Posers

WHAT IS IT?

In this game, children are given a question which links to an investigation. They have to work out which one of four methods (doing a fair test, carrying out a survey, classifying things into groups, or observing/measuring something over time) they would use to answer the question and how they would present the evidence they have collected (table, bar chart, line graph, scatter graph). The teacher puts labels for the different ways of finding out in the four corners of the room. At the teacher's call, a runner, nominated from each group of children, goes to the corner of the room that their group has chosen and adopts a pose to signify the way their group thinks that the results should be presented (e.g. table – on all fours, bar chart – standing straight arms tight by side, line graph – arms spread at an angle to represent a line, or scatter graph – fists punching the air in different places).

WHY IS IT IMPORTANT?

Planning how to go about an investigation is an important scientific skill. Children need to be able to select the best way of finding out. It is also useful for them to think ahead to the way their evidence will be presented.

> Children need to know that there are several kinds of investigation, not just a fair test.

> Children should know that deciding which kind of investigation to use is an important step when planning an investigation.

> Children should recognise that there are several ways to present results and that they need to select the one that is appropriate for their investigation.

> Some children, especially EAL (English as an additional language) children, get confused by the double meaning of the word table (piece of furniture or chart for results). This game gives an opportunity to talk about both meanings.

RESOURCES
Available in the book and on CD

KINDS OF INVESTIGATION GLOSSARY (Version 1-3 - per group)	P11
WAYS TO PRESENT EVIDENCE SHEETS (Version 1-3 - per group)	P12-15
QUESTIONS (Version 1-3 - teacher only, can be cut up)	P16-17
INVESTIGATION LABELS (Version 1 - for teacher enlarge to A3 and cut up, Version 2 and 3 - set for each group to cut up)	P18

How to play Posers

Version 1 - Whole class

- Put up the 'Investigation labels' (p18) one in each corner of the room.

- Give each group copies of the 'Kinds of investigation glossary' (p11) and 'Ways to present evidence' sheets (p12-15). Let children discuss these to make sure that they understand each type of investigation and method of presenting evidence.

- Call out a 'Question' (p16-17).

- Children discuss which of the four types of investigation they would use to answer the question and how they would present their evidence.

- Ask each group to choose a representative to show their decisions.

- Call out "Posers - to your positions".

- The representatives go to the appropriate corner to show their choice of investigation and 'pose' in the relevant position to show how they would present their results (see introduction for suggestions).

- Compare ideas and discuss differences by asking groups to justify their choices. Repeat for other questions.

Version 2 - Whole class

- Play the game as in Version 1.

- Instead of individuals running to a corner, the whole group stands up, one holds up an 'Investigation label' (p18) and the rest strike a pose showing how they would present their results.

- Compare the choices and discuss differences, asking groups to justify their decisions. Repeat for different questions.

Version 3 - CD & Whiteboard

- Open the Planning Poser activity on the CD. Select the Poser Matching page showing the types of investigations and ways of presenting results.

- Choose a question from the question cards (p16-17) and stick it at the side of the whiteboard or write it on the whiteboard. Play the game as in 2 above.

- As soon as a group has made a decision they strike a pose. A child from each group comes to the front and joins the 'type of investigation' with the 'way of presenting results', using different coloured whiteboard pens if possible.

- Compare responses and discuss differences.

Posers (Version 1)

1 PLACE THE INVESTIGATION LABELS IN FOUR CORNERS OF THE ROOM.

2 GIVE EACH GROUP OF CHILDREN A GLOSSARY TO READ AND DISCUSS.

3 CALL OUT A QUESTION AND GIVE TIME FOR DISCUSSION.

4 CALL OUT 'PLANNING POSERS TO YOUR POSITIONS!'

5 RUNNERS FROM EACH GROUP GO TO CORNERS AND ADOPT POSITIONS.

6 CHILDREN TALK ABOUT WHAT THEY HAVE CHOSEN AND WHY.

Background notes

The four kinds of investigation used in this game are the ones that children are most likely to meet in primary science; there are others. Spend a little time thinking about the different kinds of investigation and looking at examples of each one (see Glossary p11).

You could also talk about ways of recording (see examples p12-15). Children are likely to be familiar with the table, bar chart and line graph. You may need to introduce the scatter graph to some children, or omit it, if playing the game with younger children or struggling learners.

SCIENCE QUESTIONS TO CALL OUT (other responses may be possible)		
QUESTIONS TO CALL OUT	**METHOD OF INVESTIGATION**	**METHOD OF RECORDING**
Which paper towel soaks up most water?	Fair test	Bar chart
How can we group these materials?	Classifying	Table
What will happen to the temperature of the hot water if we let it cool down and take its temperature every 5 minutes?	Over time	Line graph
When I change the size of the spinner wings, what happens to the time it takes to fall?	Fair test	Line graph
What colour hair do people in our class have?	Survey	Bar chart
If we make the elastic band different lengths, what will happen to the pitch of the note when we pluck it?	Fair test	Table
Which materials are attracted to the magnet?	Classifying	Table
How does the mould grow on this orange if we leave it for three weeks?	Over time	Table
Do people with longer arms have longer fingers.	Survey	Scatter graph
Which is the best soil for letting water drain through?	Fair test	Bar chart
Which of these solids dissolve in a beaker of water and which do not dissolve?	Classifying	Table
How does the shape of the moon change if we look at it every other night over the next month?	Over time	Table
How many different types of plants can we find in the long grass, the short grass and in the woods?	Survey	Bar chart

Kinds of Investigation
Glossary

Kind of investigation	Description	Example of this kind of investigation
Doing a fair test	In a fair test, you change one variable to find out what happens to something else. You only change one variable and keep all the other variables the same.	What happens to the distance a toy car travels when you put the ramp at different heights?
Carrying out a survey	In a survey, you record things you observe or measure. You often do a survey when you want to find things out about people, or plants and animals in their environment.	Do people with longer legs jump higher? Which plants do bees visit most often?
Classifying	You classify things when you sort them into groups. Sometimes we sort things into different groups because they have different features, like materials or animals. Sometimes we sort things into groups because they behave in different ways – the things either do something or they don't do something.	How can we group these different leaves? Are these materials attracted to the magnet or not?
Observing or measuring something over time	Sometimes you find things out by watching one thing over a period of time – you could watch it for a few minutes or a few weeks. Sometimes we just make observations and sometimes we can measure what is happening using equipment.	How will the caterpillar change over the next six weeks?

Presenting Evidence 1
Tables

Tables can be used in many ways. They can have two or more columns. They can have words or numbers in them. Here are 3 examples of tables. These can be helpful when you are doing **fair tests, surveys, observing over time and classifying.**

Do we all have the same pulse rate?	
NAME	PULSE RATE
John	65
Caroline	73
Ahmed	66
Rebecca	64
Joshua	72

How loud are sounds?	
SOUND	HOW LOUD
whisper	quiet
clap	medium
alarm	very loud
yell	loud
radio	variable

How can we identify leaves?			
LEAF	PRICKLY	LENGTH (CM)	SHINY?
Ivy	NO	4	YES
Oak	NO	8	NO
Hazel	NO	5	NO
Holly	YES	7	YES
Horse Chestnut	NO	16	NO

Presenting Evidence 2
Bar Charts

Bar charts usually have words across the bottom (horizontal axis) and numbers up the side (vertical axis). These can be helpful when you are doing **fair tests or surveys**.

Which is the best material for making a tea cosy?

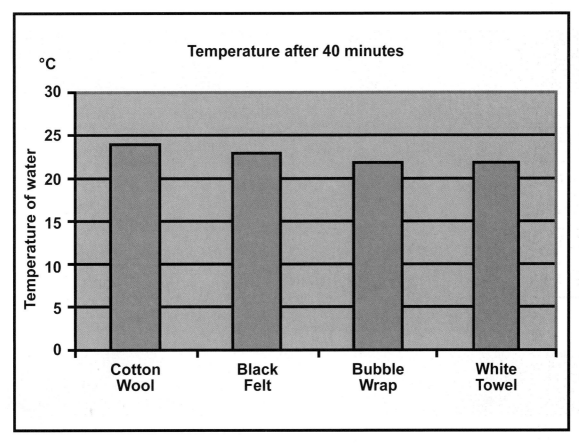

Presenting Evidence 3
Line Graphs

Line graphs have numbers on the bottom (horizontal axis) and up the side (vertical axis). These can be helpful when you are doing **fair tests and when you are measuring something over time.** Here are two line graphs.

Stretching elastic

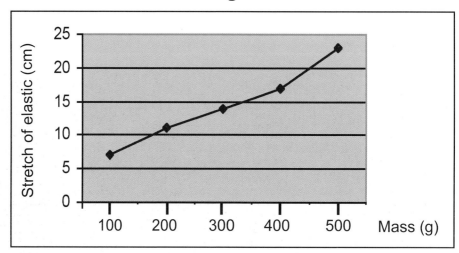

Growing Sunflowers

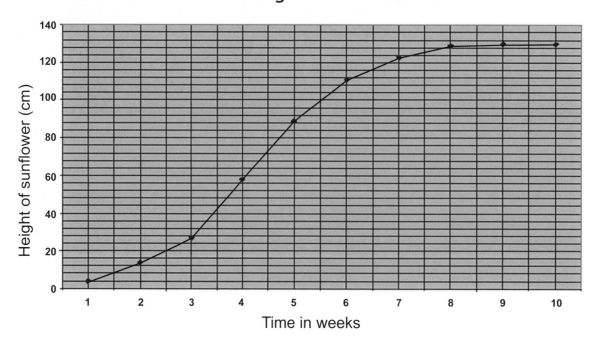

Presenting Evidence 4
Scatter Graphs

In a scatter graph, each dot represents one person or thing. You plot the dots to see whether there is a connection between two sets of data. These can be helpful when you are doing **surveys**.

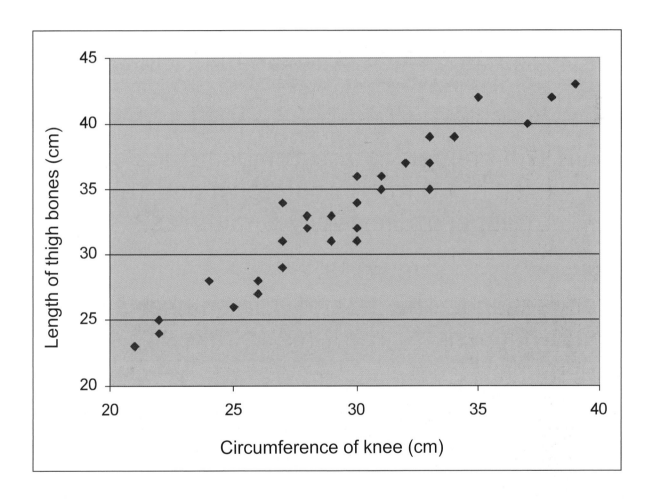

Poser
Questions

Which paper towel soaks up the most water?

How can we group these materials?

What will happen to the temperature of the hot water if we let it cool down and take its temperature every 5 minutes?

When I change the size of the spinner's wings, what happens to the time it takes to fall?

What colour hair do people in our class have?

If we make the elastic band different lengths, what will happen to the pitch of the note when we pluck it?

Which materials are attracted
to the magnet?

How does the mould grow on this orange if we
leave it for three weeks?

Do people with longer arms have
longer fingers?

Which is the best soil for letting water
drain through?

Which of these solids dissolve in a beaker of
water and which do not dissolve?

How does the shape of the moon change if
we look at it every other night over
the next month?

How many different types of plants can we
find in the long grass, the short grass and
in the woods?

Investigation labels

Enlarge to A3 and cut up to put in the corners of the classroom.
Use as A4 on children's tables.

Classifying

Fair Test

Survey

Over Time

Fair Testing

Fair Test Scramble

Fair Testing

Fair Test Scramble

2

WHAT IS IT?

This is a game where groups of children are given a large number of variables from several different investigations written on pieces of card. The teacher announces a question for a fair test investigation. Each group has to select the variables (what we should change, what we should measure and what we should keep the same) that apply in that investigation. The words CHANGE, MEASURE, KEEP THE SAME are posted in accessible places around the room. The teacher calls out one of the words. The children discuss their ideas. On the shout of "scramble" a runner from each group scrambles, or races, to the correct place holding the relevant variable card or cards.

WHY IS IT IMPORTANT?

Many investigations in primary science education involve fair tests. Children are generally aware of the need for fair tests but do not always understand that it involves changing one variable to see the effect it has on another variable. They can often believe it is about fairness in a personal sense, such as everyone having a turn during the investigation.

> Children need to understand why it is important to choose just one variable to change. If more than one variable is changed in an investigation then it is difficult to know what caused the effect.

> Choosing what to change and measure helps children organise tables, charts and graphs.

> Children need to be able to distinguish between something that is measured, to make sure that it is kept the same, and something that is measured as it alters during the experiment.

RESOURCES
Available in the book and on CD

INVESTIGATION PICTURES (Version 1 - set per group)	P25
VARIABLE CARDS (Version 1 and 3 - set per group, Version 2 – teacher only)	P26-27
QUESTIONS CARD (Version 1 and 3 - teacher only)	P28-29
LABELS SAYING CHANGE, MEASURE AND KEEP THE SAME (Version 1 and 2 - for teacher photocopied on A3 and cut up)	P30
YOU WILL ALSO NEED Wipe boards, pens and wipers.	

How to play Fair Test Scramble

Version 1 - Whole class

- Put the large 'Labels' CHANGE, MEASURE and KEEP THE SAME (p30) in easily accessible places. Give each group the 'Variable cards' (p26-27).

- Talk about the investigations in the 'Investigation pictures' (p25).

- Call out a question from the 'Questions' list (p28-29).

- Allow a little time to discuss what they would CHANGE, MEASURE and KEEP THE SAME in order to answer the question.

- Call out "Get ready to scramble ...." followed by one of the words on one of the labels e.g. "...CHANGE".

- A runner grabs the 'Variable card' that their group has decided will be changed and runs to the label.

- The first runner to put the correct 'Variable card' against the label wins a point for their team. Compare the chosen variables and discuss any differences.

Version 2 - Groups

- Ask one group to stand with a 'Variable Card' by each label For example:
CHANGE - distance object is from light
MEASURE - length of shadow
KEEP THE SAME - height of object.

- Ask the rest of the class to discuss what the question might be. For example 'Does the distance between the object and the light make a difference to the length of the shadow?' Each group could write their question on a wipe board.

- Choose one board at a time and ask the rest of the class to decide if it could be a correct answer. Each group, that finds a question that fits, gains one point.

Version 3 - CD & Whiteboard

- Open the 'Fair Test Scramble' activity on the CD at the 'Variable ' page. Give the children 'Variable cards' (p26-27) and play as in version 1.

- The runner comes to the board and ticks the variable using the whiteboard pen.

- Compare the chosen variables and discuss any differences.

Extra Activity

At the end of this section (p31-32) you will find two examples of investigations where fair testing is important. You can discuss these with children, either to introduce the game or to review their understanding afterwards.

Fair Test Scramble (Version 1)

1 PUT THE LABELS 'CHANGE', 'MEASURE' AND 'KEEP THE SAME' IN EASILY ACCESSIBLE PLACES.

2 GROUPS OF CHILDREN LAY OUT THEIR VARIABLE CARDS ON THEIR TABLES.

3 CALL OUT A QUESTION. CHILDREN DISCUSS THE VARIABLES.

4 CALL OUT 'GET READY TO SCRAMBLE...

...measure

5 A RUNNER FROM EACH GROUP TAKES THEIR CHOSEN CARD TO THE 'MEASURE' LABEL.

6 COMPARE THE DIFFERENT VARIABLE CARDS.

Background notes

The following list suggests questions that you could use in Fair Test Scramble, plus possible answers.

QUESTION	ANSWERS		
	Change	Measure	Keep the same
How does the temperature of the water affect the time it takes the sugar to dissolve?	Temperature of water	Time sugar takes to dissolve	Volume of water, mass of sugar, number of stirs, type of sugar
How does the height of the ramp affect the distance the can travels?	Height of the ramp	Distance the can travels	Size of can, type of surface, point where can was released
How does the height of drop make a difference to how high the ball bounces?	Height of the drop	Height of the bounce	Type of ball, type of surface
Does the distance between the puppet and the light make a difference to the length of the shadow?	Distance between puppet and light	Length of the shadow	Height of the puppet
What happens to the time the sugar takes to dissolve when you change the volume of water?	Volume of water	Time sugar takes to dissolve	Temperature of water, mass of sugar, number of stirs, type of sugar
How does the size of the can affect the distance the can travels?	Size of can	Distance the can travels	Height of the ramp, type of surface, point where can was released
What happens to the height of the bounce when the ball gets dropped on different surfaces?	Type of surface	Height of the bounce	Type of ball, height of drop
What happens to the length of the shadow when you change the height of the puppet?	Height of the puppet	Length of the shadow	Distance between puppet and light
How does the type of sugar affect the time it takes the sugar to dissolve?	Type of sugar	Time sugar takes to dissolve	Volume of water, mass of sugar, number of stirs, temperature of water

Other questions can be made up as required.

Investigation Pictures

These are the four investigations the children carried out.

What affects the time sugar takes to dissolve in water?

What makes a difference to the distance a can travels after it has been rolled down a ramp?

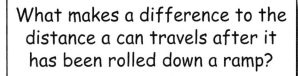
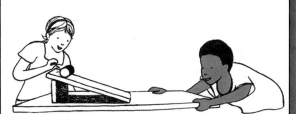

What affects the height of a shadow when a light shines on a puppet?

How can we make a ball bounce to different heights on its first bounce?

Fair Test Scramble
Variable Cards
You need to cut out the cards

Distance can travelled
Point where can was released
Height of ramp
Height of bounce
Size of can
Type of surface
Length of shadow
Height of drop

Temperature of water
Mass of sugar
Time sugar takes to dissolve
Type of ball
Volume of water
Height of puppet
Type of sugar
Distance between puppet and light
Number of stirs

Fair Test Scramble
Questions

How does the temperature of the water affect the time it takes the sugar to dissolve?

How does the height of the ramp affect the distance the can travels?

How does the height of drop make a difference to how high the ball bounces?

Does the distance between the puppet and the light make a difference to the length of the shadow?

What happens to the time the sugar takes to dissolve when you change the volume of water?

How does the size of the can affect the distance the can travels?

What happens to the height of the bounce when the ball gets dropped on different surfaces?

What happens to the length of the shadow when you change the height of the puppet?

How does the type of sugar affect the time it takes the sugar to dissolve?

Fair Test Scramble
Labels

Enlarge to A3 and cut up to put around classroom.

Change

Measure

Keep the same

Keeping Coffee Warm

Ahmed, Alison and Alex were trying to find out which material would be the best to stop the teacher's coffee going cold. They had four different materials, cotton, foil, bubble wrap and felt. They wrapped each one round some hot water in plastic cups.

Which variable were they changing?

Which variable were they measuring to get their results?

Which variables were they keeping the same?

Drying Clothes

Samir, Sandi and Sal were trying to find out if clothes dry better when it is windy. They had chosen four different items to dry: a t-shirt, a towel, a shirt and a sock. They planned to put them on a washing line in the playground on four different days.

Which variable is changing?

Which variable were they measuring to get their results?

Which variables were they keeping the same?

Identifying Equipment

What's in the Box?

Identifying Equipment

What's in the Box?

WHAT IS IT?

In this game children have to work out what item of science equipment is the mystery object hidden in a box. The teacher chooses one piece of science equipment and, out of sight of the class, puts it in a box. A box with a lid, such as an A4 paper box, is ideal. The children ask a series of questions which can be answered with a "yes" or a "no", for example "Is it used for measuring?", "Would it contain liquids?", "Will it measure more than 20 units?". Their series of questions should help them to find out what is in the box.

WHY IS IT IMPORTANT?

Children need to be able to select the right equipment for the task. Sometimes they can have problems carrying out investigations because they have made inappropriate choices. Getting them to think carefully about equipment will help them to be more aware of the range of equipment that is available. This will help them to investigate more successfully and often more accurately.

> If the name of piece of equipment is unfamiliar to children then they will be less likely to ask for it or use it.

> Children do not always remember how particular equipment is used.

> By asking questions about the piece of equipment they can clarify what it is and how it used.

> If children do not understand what a particular piece of equipment is used for, they might use it inappropriately.

> Children need to realize that some equipment comes with different scales to allow for more precise measurements or to measure larger objects.

RESOURCES
Available in the book and on CD

EQUIPMENT LIST 1
(Version 1 and 2 -
set per group)

P39

and/or

EQUIPMENT LIST 2
(Version 1 and 2 -
set per group)

P40

YOU WILL ALSO NEED
Samples of equipment from chosen lists. You do not need them all. (Version 1 - teacher only, Version 2 - possibly for children (optional))
A box (Version 1 - teacher only, Version 2 - teacher and per group)
Wipe boards, pens and wipers (Version 1)

How to play What's in the Box?

Version 1 - Whole class

- Hand out Equipment list (p39 or p40) to groups of children.

- Choose a piece of equipment and secretly place it in the box.

- Ask the groups to discuss a good 'yes/no' question to help them to identify what is in the box. Select one group to ask their question.

- Say "yes" or "no". If groups think that they know the answer they write it on a wipe board and hold it up on the count of 3. If the guess is wrong allow groups a short period of time to consider their next question.

- Select another group to ask their question. Continue until the object is correctly identified by one or more of the teams.

- Award 2 points for a correct answer. Deduct 2 points for incorrect answer (stops early guessing).

Version 2 - Table top

- Give each group an identical set of equipment on each table and one box big enough to fit any piece of equipment. You need a set too. Alternatively give out List 1 (p39) and/or 2 (p40).

- Hide a piece of equipment in your box. Proceed as above with groups asking questions. After each round any group that thinks they know the answer puts one of the objects (or the card) in the box. They bring the box to the front of the room.

- Continue to play the game until all the groups have brought their boxes to the front. Now open the boxes in order and reveal the contents. Then open your box.

- Any incorrect groups lose 2 points. Correct answers are given points according to how soon the decision was made. The first group(s) gets 5 points, the second 4, and so on.

Version 3 - CD & Whiteboard

- Go to What's in the box? on the CD and show equipment list on the whiteboard. Play the game as before with the whole class.

- After each round ask groups to nominate pieces of equipment that are now ruled out as a result of the answer to their question and cross them off if everyone agrees. Continue until there is only one piece of equipment left.

- Challenge the class to see how few questions they can ask to identify the piece of equipment.

What's in the Box? (Version 1)

1 PUT AN OBJECT IN THE BOX.

2 CHILDREN DISCUSS POSSIBLE QUESTIONS.

Can it be used for measuring?

3 CHOOSE ONE GROUP TO ASK A YES/NO QUESTION AND GIVE YOUR RESPONSE.

No

Is it magnetic?

4 ASK CHILDREN TO DISCUSS AND WRITE ANSWER ON A WIPE BOARD IF THEY KNOW IT.

It's filter paper

It isn't

5 GROUPS KEEP ASKING QUESTIONS UNTIL A GROUP GETS IT RIGHT.

Is it a magnify-ing glass?

6 WHEN A GROUP GUESSES THE OBJECT, GIVE THEM 2 POINTS.

Well done.

Background notes

You can use any equipment normally available in school. On the next pages are two possible lists to use for this activity, the second being more demanding than the first. They are available as sets of cards to be cut out by you or the children. You do not need all the equipment listed. The intention is to widen the range of equipment that children consider when making their decisions.

NOTES ON LIST 1 (P39)

This list covers all the basic equipment you would normally find being used in primary science. Several of the items should have been encountered at an early stage in the children's science experience. You can remove or replace items, by removing or adding cards.

NOTES ON LIST 2 (P40)

The second list is more demanding because it includes several items normally used in the later stages in primary schools. It also includes items with different scales. It is important that they understand that some items are adapted for use in different circumstances e.g. measuring larger or smaller volumes to certain degrees of accuracy.

> **NOTE**
> If you are using the activity to develop, rather than revise, children's understanding of equipment, show them examples of all the items before playing the game.

> **NOTE**
> If you want to make the game more demanding then you can play it without giving any lists to children.

Equipment List 1

Standard thermometer (0 – 100° C)	Crocodile lead
Timer (clockwork type)	Forcemeter (0 - 10 N)
Tape measure (0 – 100 cm)	Horseshoe magnet
30 cm ruler	Bar magnet
Plastic measuring cylinder (250 ml)	Sieve
Magnifying glass	Filter paper
Electric bulb (lamp)	Plastic funnel
Battery (cell)	Safety goggles
Battery holder	Electric bulb holder

Equipment List 2

Standard thermometer (0 – 100° C)	Standard thermometer (0 - 40° C)
Stopwatch measuring whole seconds	Stopwatch measuring hundredths of seconds
Tape measure (0 – 100 cm)	Tape measure (0 - 10 metres)
Measuring cylinder (0 – 100 ml)	Measuring cylinder (0 - 250 ml)
Measuring cylinder (0 – 1 litre)	Stethoscope
Pooter/Bug hunter	Syringe
Forcemeter (0 - 2.5 N)	Forcemeter (0 - 10 N)
Forcemeter (0 - 50 N)	Datalogger – light probe
Calipers	Masses (weights)
Balance	Bathroom scales
Graph paper	Tuning fork

Repeat Readings

Bull's Eye

Repeat Readings

Bull's Eye

4

WHAT IS IT?

In this game, children think about various reasons for taking repeat readings and then put them in order. After group discussion, they decide where to put each reason on the target. They put the best reason nearest to the bull's eye and the worst furthest away. They compare their answers, which leads to more discussion.

WHY IS IT IMPORTANT?

We need to help children to understand that repeating your test is a positive thing because it gives you better quality evidence and allows you to check results.

> Children often misunderstand the reason for taking repeat readings.

> Children may say that we take repeat readings to make it a fair test, although taking repeat readings does not help to keep variables the same.

> Many believe that if they have carried out an investigation carefully, there is no need to do it again.

> Some children view the word 'repeat' negatively. They associate 'repeat' with having to do something again because they got it wrong the first time.

> It is also common for children to think that repeating a reading makes it more accurate. Accuracy is to do with measuring equipment. Results can only be as accurate as the equipment that you are using. For example, if you are using a ruler that measures in whole centimetres you will not be able to get a more accurate result by repeating the test. You will still only be able to measure in centimetres not in more precise millimetres.

RESOURCES
Available in the book and on CD

STATEMENTS (Version 1-3 - set per group to cut up)	**P47**
BULL'S EYE CENTRE large disc (Version 1 - teacher only)	**P48**
TABLE TOP BULL'S EYE enlarged to A3 (Version 2 and 3 - per group)	**P49**
COPIES OF INVESTIGATION 1 and 2 (optional) (extra activity - set per group)	**P50-51**
YOU WILL ALSO NEED Rope or chalk if using the bull's eye on the floor (Version 1 - teacher only)	

How to play Bull's Eye

Version 1 - Classroom

- Create a large bull's eye on the floor with rings made using ropes or chalk. Put the circle with 'Reasons we Repeat Readings' (p48) in the centre.

- Cut up and hand out 'Statements' (p47), one set to each group. Call out one of the statements.

- Groups discuss and agree where it should go. A runner for each group brings the statement and stands at the agreed place on the bull's eye.

- Groups compare and discuss differences.

- Repeat the activity with the other statements. Identify and talk about any that are still misplaced.

Version 2 - Table top

- Hand out the 'Table top bull's eye' (p49) and the 'Statements' (p47) to each group for them to cut up.

- Groups consider and agree where to place statements round the bull's eye on table top. You can do this one at a time, as above, if you wish.

- Ask which they have put closest to the centre and why. Ask which they have put furthest from the centre and why.

- Compare and discuss differences. Identify and talk about any that are still misplaced.

Version 3 - CD & Whiteboard

- Open the 'Bull's Eye' target on the CD.

- In pairs the children discuss where a statement should go.

- Choose a child from each group to use the whiteboard pen to tick their chosen position on the bull's eye.

- Compare and discuss differences.

- Repeat with other statements .

- Identify and talk about any that are misplaced.

Extra Activity

At the end of this section (p50-51) you will find two examples of investigations where it is important that children repeat their readings. You can discuss these with children, either to introduce the game or to review their understanding afterwards.

Bull's Eye (Version 1)

1 MAKE THE BULL'S EYE.

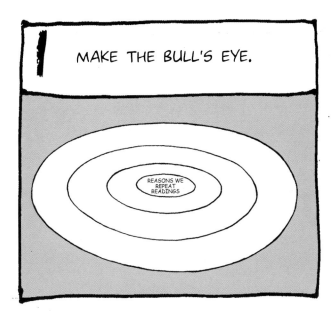

2 HAND OUT REASON CARDS.

3 CALL OUT ONE REASON.

4 GROUPS DISCUSS WHERE IT SHOULD GO.

5 RUNNER FOR EACH GROUP STANDS ON THEIR CHOSEN PLACE ON THE BULL'S EYE.

6 GROUPS COMPARE AND DISCUSS DIFFERENCES.

Background notes

The following is an appropriate order for the statements, closest to the centre of the bull's eye first.

Other orders are acceptable. The important thing is to get the children talking and thinking about why we take repeat readings.

The first six responses below would usually be credited in the science KS2 End of Key Stage tests in England:

Reasons we repeat tests:

1) So we will get a better idea of the likely result

2) Because readings are always a bit different so we need to do them more than once

3) Because things change a little bit so we need to take an average

4) So we can get more evidence

5) To check results

6) Because the first reading might not be right

The following reasons are not correct and should be far from the bull's eye:

7) To use scientific equipment

8) So we can change the equipment

9) So we can make the test fair

NOTES ON INVESTIGATIONS

(Optional activities for discussion before or after the game)

Example 1 – (p50)
Breaking Threads in a unit on forces

The children change the type of thread but keep the length of each thread the same to keep the test as fair as possible. The table shows that in spite of this the readings are different. It may be difficult for children to be sure that the thread isn't jerked sometimes more than others or to spot the precise point at which it breaks. If children repeat their readings and estimate the average, it will help them find out 'the most likely result' and minimise the effect of small errors.

Example 2 - (p51)
Dissolving Artificial Sweeteners in a unit on materials

In this investigation, the children will find it difficult to ensure that the water is not disturbed – the equivalent of stirring - or that the temperature in the room remains constant. They may also find it hard to decide when all of the sweetener has dissolved. If children repeat readings and estimate an average, it will help them predict what the reading would be if these small differences could be eliminated.

Bull's Eye
Statements

Here are some reasons why we might repeat readings.

To use scientific equipment
So we can get more evidence
Because the first reading might not be right
To make the test fair
To check results
So we will get a better idea of the likely result
Because readings are always a bit different so we need to do them more than once
Because things change a little bit so we need to take an average
So we can change the equipment

REASONS WE REPEAT READINGS

Table Top Bull's Eye

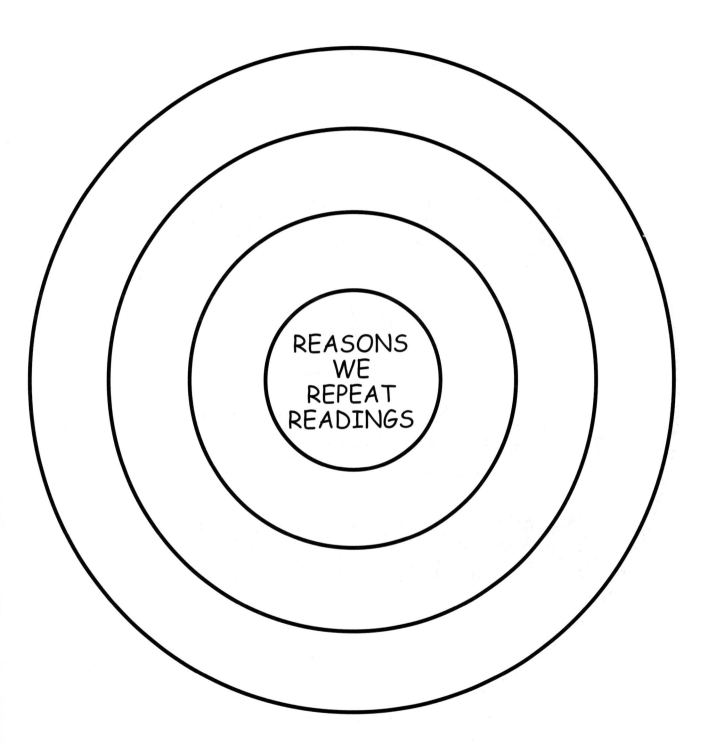

REASONS
WE
REPEAT
READINGS

Breaking Threads

Some children are investigating the force needed to break different threads. They loop one end of each thread round the hook on a forcemeter and pull gently until the thread snaps. They record the number of Newtons (N) at the point when the thread breaks and repeat the procedure 3 times with each thread.

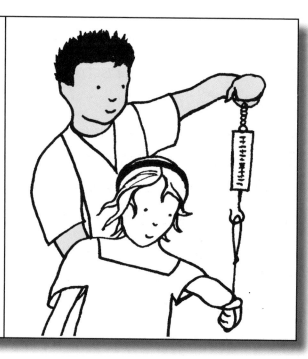

Here is the record of their results

Type of Thread	Force to break the thread (N)				
	1st go	2nd go	3rd go	4th go	Most Likely Result
Grey Plain Wool	6	7	6	6	6
Red Nylon	9	7	8	8	8
Blue Cotton	8	10	12	10	10
Yellow Fluffy Wool	5	5	5	6	5

○ Why do you think they did not get the same number of Newtons each time they tested the threads?

○ How did repeating the tests help them?

○ How did they decide which was the most likely result?

Dissolving Artificial Sweeteners

Some children are testing how long sweeteners take to dissolve in water at different temperatures. They take the temperature of the water, just before a sweetener is added, using a temperature sensor. They let the sweetener dissolve without stirring.

Here is the record of their results

Temp of water ^0C	Time for sweetener to dissolve (seconds)				
	1st go	2nd go	3rd go	4th go	Most Likely Result
10	22	20	23	22	22
21	16	15	14	14	15
36	13	10	12	12	12
58	7	6	5	6	6

○ The children got slightly different results each time they repeated their tests. Why do you think this happened?

○ How did repeating the tests help them?

○ How did they decide which was the most likely result?

Using Tables
Table Talk

Using Tables

Table Talk

WHAT IS IT?

The object of this game is for children to work out whether their results, shown on a table, support a conclusion. The game is set on a mythical planet where five different species of animal are found. The table describes the number of wings, eyes, antennae and legs on each animal. The numbers are decided by chance, called out by the teacher and filled in on the table by the children. The children call out when they think that the table shows enough evidence to make a decision about their particular conclusion.

WHY IS IT IMPORTANT?

Tables are important organising tools in science. This game gives children practice in completing and interpreting the evidence shown on a table and also asks children to think about whether they have sufficient evidence to support a conclusion.

> Children can get muddled about what the information on a table represents.

> Children often draw conclusions too soon, without collecting all the necessary evidence.

> Children need to use formal scientific language for themselves to become familiar with it. In this game children have to call out one of the phrases "Results support the conclusion" or "Results do not support the conclusion".

RESOURCES
Available in the book and on CD

BLANK TABLES (Version 1-3 - one per pair/group of children)	**P59**
CONCLUSION CARDS (Version 1 - one statement per pair of children)	**P60-63**
INCOMPLETE STATEMENTS (Version 1-3 - teacher only)	**P64-65**

YOU WILL ALSO NEED
A die (or some other means of quickly and randomly generating the numbers 1 to 6)

Post-its (Version 2 only - different colour for each group)

2 pieces of paper headed 'supports conclusion' and 'does not support conclusion' (Version 2 only - a set per group)

How to play Table Talk

Version 1 - Whole class

- Give pairs of children a 'Blank table' (p59) and one 'Conclusion card' (p60-63).

- Cut out and fold the 'Incomplete statements' (p64-65). Put them in a container.

- Pick out one statement. Roll the die. Call out the statement using the number rolled e.g. The Thrub has three antennae.

- Children write the number on their table in the appropriate place.

- Continue, as above, to add more numbers to their tables. Allow some time for discussion.

- When a pair of children thinks they have enough evidence they call out – "Results support the conclusion" or "Results do not support the conclusion".

- Decide, as a class, whether they had enough evidence to make the call.

- First pair to call correctly gets 5 points. The second pair 4 points and so on. Incorrect call loses 1 point.

- To encourage everyone to continue filling in the table, tell the children that they are all going to draw one of the animals to finish the game.

Version 2 - Whole class

- Give groups a 'Blank table' (p59), 2 pieces of paper headed 'supports conclusion' and 'does not support conclusion' and Post-its.

- Roll a die until the blank table is filled (see version 1), or give out a completed table.

- Give each group 5 or 10 minutes to generate conclusions based on the data, write each one on separate Post-its and sort onto the two pieces of paper.

- Groups swap papers. They give 1 point for each conclusion they think is correctly placed. Discuss any that are very interesting or where there is disagreement.

Version 3 - CD & Whiteboard

- Open the Blank Table on the CD. Play as above but add numbers on the whiteboard so that they are visible to everyone.

Extra Activity

At the end of this section (p66-67) you will find examples of investigations involving tables. Discuss these with the children, either to introduce the game or to review their understanding afterwards.

Table Talk (Version 1)

1 CHILDREN ARE GIVEN A BLANK TABLE AND A CONCLUSION CARD.

2 PICK AN INCOMPLETE STATEMENT AND ROLL A DIE TO FILL IN THE NUMBER.

3 READ OUT THE COMPLETED STATEMENT.

4 CHILDREN FILL IN INFORMATION ON THE TABLE.

5 CHILDREN CALL OUT WHEN THEY THINK THEY HAVE ENOUGH EVIDENCE TO DECIDE.

6 CLASS DECIDES IF THEY ARE RIGHT OR NOT.

Background notes

Children are likely to need time to discuss whether or not their results support their conclusion. Make sure that they have a short discussion time between each roll of the die.

Insist that children call out either 'Results support the conclusion' or 'Results do not support the conclusion'. It is only by getting children to say the words that they will become part of their everyday vocabulary. Once a pair of children has made the call, write their conclusion on a board. Ask others to say whether they agree or disagree with the call, giving reasons.

NOTES ON 'EXTRA ACTIVITY' INVESTIGATIONS (OPTIONAL)

To be used for discussion before or after the games.

Investigation 1 (p66) - Properties of Materials

The table shows the results of four different tests on the same six objects. It also says what material each object is made from. The results show whether or not each object or material displayed that characteristic. Children need to interpret the table to decide whether or not the results support each conclusion. They can write their answers in the space provided, giving them more practice of using tables. The answers are shown in Table 1 below.

Investigation 2 (p67) - Hardness of Rocks

One way to try to find out the hardness of different rocks is to see which objects can scratch them. The softer the rock the more easily it will be scratched. The table shows which objects scratched which rocks. As in the first example, children need to interpret the table to decide whether or not the results support each conclusion. The answers are shown in Table 2 below.

TABLE 1

Conclusion	Results support conclusion	Results do not support conclusion
All metal things are attracted to magnets.		✔
Some plastic things let light through.	✔	
All the metals we tested were good electrical conductors.	✔	
None of the bendy things conducted electricty.		✔

TABLE 2

Conclusion	Results support conclusion	Results do not support conclusion
The clay was soft. It was scratched by all our objects.	✔	
The sandstone was harder than the chalk.	✔	
The granite was not as hard as the slate.		✔
The order of hardness for our five rocks, going from hardest to softest, is granite, slate, sandstone, chalk, clay.	✔	

Table Talk
Blank Table

Five species of animal live on planet Xena. You have a blank results table and a conclusion. You will get numbers to put on the table.

As soon as you have enough evidence to be sure about the conclusion, call out ....

Results support the conclusion.

OR

Results do not support the conclusion.

Name	Number of legs	Number of antennae	Number of eyes	Number of wings
Squag				
Thrub				
Corby				
Drobble				
Whoosh				

Conclusion Cards

Cut up and give one to each pair of children.

Easier

The Whoosh has more eyes than any other animal.

A Squag has fewer legs than a Corby.

There are more antennae on Whooshes than on Squags.

Thrubs have the same number of legs as one other animal.

Corbys have the least number of wings.

Squags have fewer wings
than a Whoosh.

Thrubs and Drobbles have the
same number of antennae.

Whooshes have more wings
than Drobbles.

Corbys have more legs
than Thrubs.

Drobbles have the same number of
eyes as one other animal.

Squags have as many eyes
as Drobbles.

Conclusion Cards
Harder

Drobbles and Whooshes have more wings between them than Thrubs and Squags.

The Thrub has more antennae than a Drobble but fewer antennae than a Corby.

Thrubs and Whooshes have more legs between them than Drobbles and Corbys.

The number of wings on a Drobble is less than the number of eyes on a Whoosh.

Whooshes have more antennae than a Drobble and fewer legs than a Thrub.

Conclusion Cards
Extension

The following sentences could be given out and used to promote discussion. None of them can be supported or refuted by the evidence for the reasons given.

> ## The Corby is the fastest flier.

(evidence only about the number of wings not how fast)

> ## Whooshes run slower than any other animal.

(evidence only about the number of legs not how fast)

> ## Drobbles can not see as far as Squags.

(evidence only about the number of eyes not how far they can see)

> ## Thrubs are better at sensing things than Squags.

(evidence only about the number of antennae not how good they are at sensing)

Incomplete Statements

Cut up, fold and place in container

The Squag has ☐ legs	The Thrub has ☐ eyes
The Squag has ☐ antennae	The Thrub has ☐ wings
The Squag has ☐ eyes	The Corby has ☐ legs
The Squag has ☐ wings	The Corby has ☐ antennae
The Thrub has ☐ legs	The Corby has ☐ eyes

The Drobble has ▢ legs	The Whoosh has ▢ eyes
The Drobble has ▢ antennae	The Whoosh has ▢ wings
The Drobble has ▢ eyes	The Whoosh has ▢ antennae
The Drobble has ▢ wings	The Whoosh has ▢ legs
The Corby has ▢ wings	The Thrub has ▢ antennae

Properties of Materials

Some children are testing some different objects to see what they do. First they decide what material each object is made from. Then they test the material. They do four different tests. Here is their table.

Object	What material is it made from?	Test 1 — Is it magnetic? Does it get pulled towards a magnet?	Test 2 — Is it flexible? Does it bend?	Test 3 — Is it transparent? Does it let light through?	Test 4 — Is it a good electrical conductor? Does the bulb light when you put it in a circuit?
Spoon	Wood	No	No	No	No
Fork	Steel	Yes	No	No	Yes
Cooking foil	Aluminium	No	Yes	No	Yes
Key	Brass	No	No	No	Yes
Food wrap	Plastic	No	Yes	Yes	No
Towel	Cotton	No	Yes	No	No

Here are some conclusions that the children made. Do the results in the table support their conclusions? Tick ONE box on each row.

Conclusion	Results support conclusion	Results do not support conclusion
All metal things are attracted to magnets.		
Some plastic things let light through.		
All the metals we tested were good electrical conductors.		
None of the bendy things conducted electricty.		

Hardness of Rocks

Some children wanted to know how hard five different rocks were. They scratched each rock with four different objects. Sometimes the object scratched the rock. Sometimes the object did not leave a mark on the rock.

Here is their table of results.

Rock	Was scratched by ...			
	plastic fork	matchstick	metal key	fingernail
Granite	X	X	X	X
Sandstone	✔	X	✔	X
Chalk	✔	✔	✔	X
Clay	✔	✔	✔	✔
Slate	X	X	✔	X

Here are some conclusions that the children made. Do the results in the table support their conclusions? Tick ONE box on each row.

Conclusion	Results support conclusion	Results do not support conclusion
The clay was soft. It was scratched by all our objects.		
The sandstone was harder than the chalk.		
The granite was not as hard as the slate.		
The order of hardness for our five rocks, going from hardest to softest, is granite, slate, sandstone, chalk, clay.		

Drawing Conclusions

Thumbs Up Thumbs Down

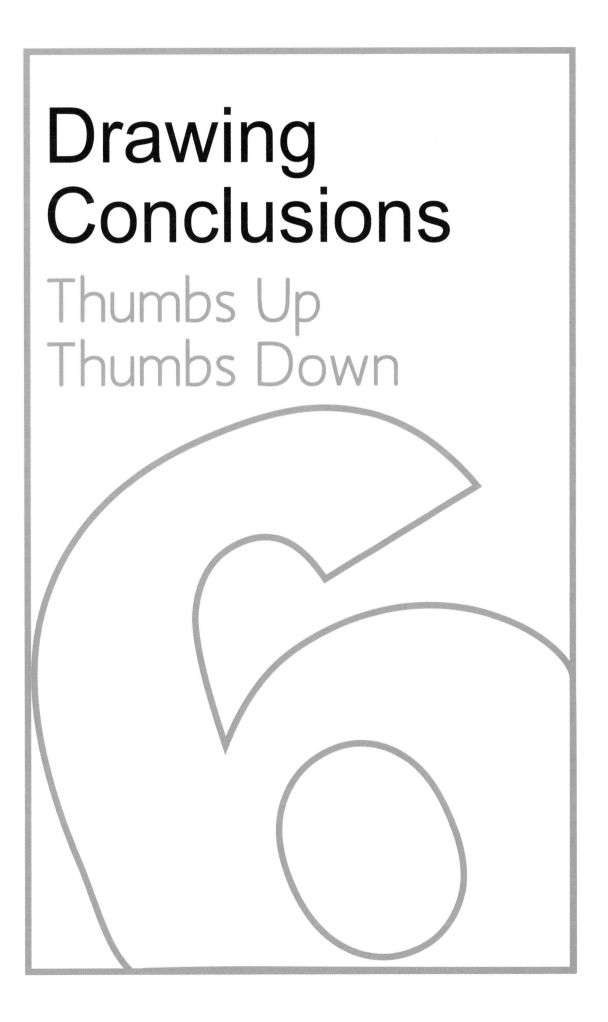

Drawing Conclusions
Thumbs Up Thumbs Down

WHAT IS IT?

This game asks children to consider conclusions and decide whether there is enough evidence to support them. Children consider a table of results that other children have gathered from investigations on materials. The teacher calls out a statement and children discuss with a partner whether the statement is completely supported by the evidence, partly supported by the evidence or not supported by the evidence. After a signal from the teacher, the children put their thumbs up (completely supported), sideways (partly supported) or down (not supported) to show what they think.

WHY IS IT IMPORTANT?

We need to help children to understand that their conclusions should be valid and match the evidence. Conclusions cannot be right or wrong, they can only be supported by the evidence, partially supported by the evidence or not supported by the evidence.

> Children often feel that drawing a conclusion is a matter of getting the 'right' answer.

> Children will ignore evidence that does not fit.

> Children can find it hard to conclude that there is some evidence but not enough to be definite about the result.

> Children often do not think beyond the evidence that is presented to consider whether there are further tests that could still be carried out. For example, in the 'Testing Materials' activity not all fabrics have been tested, so it is impossible to say whether the outcome will apply to all materials.

> Children need to use science language for themselves, which is why the phrase 'supported by the evidence' is used in this game.

RESOURCES
Available in the book and on CD

TABLE OF RESULTS (Version 1 and 2 - set per group)	P75
STATEMENT CARDS (Version 1 and 2 - teacher only)	P76-77
LABELS (Version 1 - teacher only)	P78
COPIES OF INVESTIGATION 1 and 2 (optional) (Extra activity - set per group)	P79-80

How to play Thumbs Up Thumbs Down

HERE ARE SOME DIFFERENT VERSIONS OF THE GAME

Version 1 - Whole class

- Put the children into pairs. Give each pair the 'Table of results' (p75) to share.

- Choose a statement from the 'Statement cards' (p76-77) and call it out. Put the statement where it can be seen for children to refer to.

- Give the children time to discuss whether the statement is supported by the evidence, partially supported by the evidence or not supported by the evidence.

- Ask them to put their thumbs up (completely supported), sideways (partly supported) or down (not supported) to show what they think.

- Draw columns on the board and put a number under each of the 'Thumbs Up labels' (p78) to show the number of times it was chosen.

- If children have different ideas, ask them to talk to other pairs and think about why they might not have come to the same decision.

- See whether children have changed their minds and why.

- Repeat with the other statements.

Version 2 - CD & Whiteboard

- Open 'Thumbs Up Thumbs Down' activity on the CD and show the table with 3 columns. Give pairs of children the 'Table of results' (p75) to share.

- Play the game as above.

- If children have different ideas, use the whiteboard pen to write a number in the columns to indicate the number of times each option was chosen.

- Ask them to decide with another pair if it can actually go in more than one column and the reason for their answer.

- Repeat with the other statements,

NB You can also play this game with the children's own results.

Extra Activity

At the end of this section (p79-80) you will find two examples of investigations. Children have to decide whether or not the results support the evidence. You can discuss these with children, either to introduce the game or to review their understanding afterwards.

Thumbs Up (Version 1)

1 HAND OUT THE 'TABLE OF RESULTS' TO PAIRS OR GROUPS.

2 CALL OUT ONE OF THE STATEMENTS.

Denim keeps you dry.

3 GIVE CHILDREN TIME TO DISCUSS WHAT THEY THINK.

4 CALL OUT ...

...Get your thumbs ready...

5 CHILDREN HOLD OUT THEIR THUMBS.

6 ENCOURAGE CHILDREN TO TALK ABOUT THEIR ANSWERS.

You have different ideas.

6 | THUMBS UP THUMBS DOWN | Drawing Conclusions

Background notes

The following list suggests statements to use in the game and the answers.

STATEMENT		
Out of the four materials we tested, nylon was the worst insulator.	Supported by the evidence.	👍
Wool is the best at keeping things warm. It is better than any other material.	It was the best insulator out of the materials tested but not all materials in the world were tested – not supported by the evidence. Possible to argue for thumb sideways as there is some evidence that wool is a good insulator.	👍👎
Wool did best in the waterproof test.	More water coming through means less waterproof.	👎
Denim keeps you dry.	Not supported by the evidence – it lets water through.	👎
We did the rub test on four materials and the strongest was denim.	Supported by the evidence.	👍
If you wear this type of wool in the rain you would get wetter than if you wear this type of cotton.	Supported by the evidence.	👍
The cotton wasn't as strong as the wool in the rub test.	Not supported by the evidence.	👎
Denim will always be stronger than nylon.	This type of denim seems to be stronger than this type of nylon but this might not be case for all denims and nylons – partly supported by the evidence	👊
If you want to choose a material to help you to keep warm and dry, the one to go for is denim. No other material is as good.	This evidence supports the statement but the children have only tested four materials. They haven't tested every other material.	👊👎

EXTRA ACTIVITIES

Investigation	Appropriate answers	
	Supported	Not Supported
1 Germinating Seeds (p79)	Statements 1, 3, 4, partially statement 2	Statement 5
2 Stretching Tights (p80)	Statement 1 partially statement 2	Statement 3

Thumbs Up Thumbs Down

Table of Results

Some children tested materials. They did three different tests on the same four materials.

Test 1
Insulation Test

The children wrapped different fabrics round beakers of hot water and saw how warm they kept the water.

Test 2
Waterproof Test

The children poured the same amount of water on the fabrics and saw how much water dripped through.

Test 3
Strength Test

The children rubbed the fabrics with the same stone and saw how many times they had to rub each fabric before a hole appeared.

Here is their table of results.

Type of fabric	Test 1 INSULATION TEST Temperature of water after 10 mins in degrees C	Test 2 WATERPROOF TEST How much water dripped through in 1 minute in ml	Test 3 STRENGTH TEST How many rubs before hole appears
Cotton	41	9	18
Wool	45	12	12
Denim	43	5	28
Nylon	39	6	4

Thumbs Up Thumbs Down
Statement Cards

Out of the four materials we tested, nylon was the worst insulator.

Wool is the best at keeping things warm. It is better than any other material.

Wool did best in the waterproof test.

Denim keeps you dry.

We did the rub test on four materials and the strongest was denim.

If you wear this type of wool in the rain you would get wetter than if you wear this type of cotton.

The cotton wasn't as strong as the wool in the rub test.

Denim will always be stronger than nylon.

If you want to choose a material to help you keep warm and dry the one to go for is denim. No other material is as good.

Supported by the evidence	
Partially supported by the evidence	
Not supported by the evidence	

Germinating Seeds

Some children wanted to find out what helped grass seeds to germinate. They got 4 dishes and put some damp kitchen paper in each one. They put 20 grass seeds in each dish. They left the dishes in different places and made sure the kitchen paper was always damp.

They counted the number of seeds that had germinated and kept a record on a table. This is what they found out.

Place	Temperature of place	Number of germinated seeds			
		Day 1	Day 4	Day 7	Day 10
fridge	cold	0	0	0	0
dark shed	cool	0	6	9	12
cupboard	warm	0	14	19	20

Look at the things that they said after their experiment. Do you think they are supported by the evidence, partially supported by the evidence or not supported by the evidence? Tick one box after each sentence.

Observations	Supported by the evidence	Partially supported by the evidence	Not supported by the evidence
1. The cupboard was the place where the seeds germinated quickest.			
2. It doesn't matter how long you leave seeds in a fridge, they will never germinate.			
3. It looks as if warm places are better for germinating seeds than cold places.			
4. All the seeds germinated in the warm cupboard.			
5. The dark shed was better for germinating seeds than the cupboard.			

Stretching Tights

Some children wanted to find out how much a thick pair of woollen tights would stretch when you put different masses (weights) in them.

They put their results on a graph.

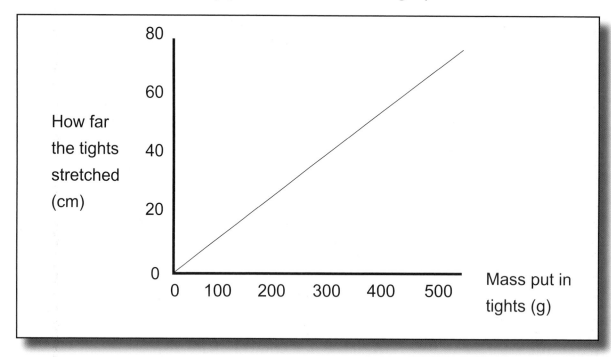

Look at the things they said after their experiment. Do you think they are supported by the evidence, partially supported by the evidence or not supported by the evidence? Tick one box after each sentence.

Observations	Supported by the evidence	Partially supported by the evidence	Not supported by the evidence
1. The more mass we put in the tights the more they stretched.			
2. If we add another mass of 100g the tights will stretch 15cm.			
3. Thin tights stretch more than thick tights.			

Vocabulary

Vocabulary Splat

Vocabulary

Vocabulary Splat

WHAT IS IT?

In this game children think about the vocabulary used in scientific enquiry. The teacher sticks scientific enquiry words round the classroom walls. The children listen to a definition, exemplification or description of one of these words and decide, in groups, which of the displayed words it matches. Each group selects a runner who, when asked, splats (sticks a Post-it) to the appropriate word. The game continues with other words.

WHY IS IT IMPORTANT?

Children need a sound knowledge of the terms they will meet when they do their investigations to be able to engage effectively in scientific processes.

Without a grasp of these key words and phrases, children will be not be able to take part in discussions about:

> their planning.

> the way they collect and present the evidence.

> what their results tell them.

> how much trust they have in their evidence.

RESOURCES
Available in the book and on CD

DESCRIPTION CARDS (Version 1 and 2 - teacher Only). (Version 3 – one set per group to be cut up)	**P87**
WORD LIST (Version 1, 3 and 4 - one set per group)	**P88**
BINGO CARDS (Version 2 - one card per group)	**P89-91**
LARGE WORD CARDS ENLARGED TO A3 (Version 1 – teacher only)	**P92-96**
YOU WILL ALSO NEED Counters (Version 2). Different coloured mini Post-its - if playing Splat as a classroom game.	

How to play SPLAT

Version 1 - Whole class

- Stick the word cards on the walls (p92-96). Give out different coloured mini Post-its to each group.

- Read out a description (p87). Put it where the children can see it. Give groups time to agree which word it describes. A runner for each group brings a Post-it and stands in the centre of the room.

- Now shout "SPLAT". The 'splatters' stick their Post-it to the word chosen by their group.

- Let the children compare their responses. Groups can change the position of their Post-it if they can justify the decision. Repeat with other statements.

Version 2 - Splat Bingo

- Give out a Splat Bingo card (p89-91) and counters to each group.

- Read out a description. Give children time to agree which word it describes and cover up the chosen word on their Bingo card. Repeat.

- Children shout "SPLAT" when they complete a row. Groups can discuss differences and move counters to correct positions. Continue with game.

Version 3 - Matching game

- Give out the 'Splat description cards' (p87) and 'Splat word list' (p88).

- Call out a word and let children choose a statement. When you call "SPLAT" one child from each group holds up the chosen statement.

Version 4 - CD & Whiteboard

- Open 'Splat' on the CD. Choose a description. Give groups 'Splat word list' (p88).

- Children to discuss and shout "SPLAT" when they have chosen a word that goes with the description.

- Match the word to the description using a whiteboard pen. Have a class vote. If correct award a point.

- Repeat with other descriptions.

SPLAT (Version 1)

1 PUT WORDS AROUND THE CLASSROOM WHERE THEY CAN BE EASILY SEEN.

2 READ OUT THE DEFINITION OF ONE OF THE WORDS.

3 GROUPS DISCUSS WHICH WORD IT COULD BE AND CHOOSE A RUNNER.

4 RUNNERS STAND UP. AND YOU CALL "SPLAT".

5 RUNNER FOR EACH GROUP ATTACHES A POST-IT TO A WORD.

6 GET CHILDREN TO EXPLAIN THEIR CHOICES AND WHERE THERE ARE DIFFERENCES.

Background notes

The table below gives statements for you to read out for each word. You could develop other alternative statements to match the words.

Descriptions (to be read out)	Word
A line that goes along the bottom or up the side of a line graph or bar chart.	axis
You can record the results of your investigation in one of these. It has words and numbers written in rows and columns.	table
Rashid said 'I looked at the woodlouse. I saw it had lots of segments and a dark stripe down its back.' He was making ...	observations
When you say what you found out in an investigation you will be making your ...	conclusion
You can record the results of your investigation on one of these. It has words on one axis and numbers on the other.	bar chart
Tools you use to help you carry out your investigation.	equipment
Talking about how you will carry out your investigation is making a ...	plan
You can record the results of your investigation on one of these. It has numbers on both axes.	line graph
You use equipment to get these. They are written in numbers and units.	measurements
You are doing one of these when you collect information or evidence to help you answer a scientific question.	investigation
Changing one variable and keeping all others the same is a ...	fair test
Saying why you think something happened is suggesting an ...	explanation
Jenny said 'I think the hotter water will make the sugar dissolve faster'. She was making a ...	prediction
You get this when you get results from your investigation.	evidence
Things that you change, measure or keep the same when you are doing an investigation are ...	variables

Splat
Description Cards

A line that goes along the bottom or up the side of a line graph or bar chart.
You can record the results of your investigation in one of these. It has words and numbers written in rows and columns.
Rashid said 'I looked at the woodlouse. I saw it had lots of segments and a dark stripe down its back.' He was making ...
When you say what you found out in an investigation you will be making your ...
You can record the results of your investigation on one of these. It has words on one axis and numbers on the other.
Tools you use to help you carry out your investigation.
Talking about how you will carry out your investigation is making a ...
You can record the results of your investigation on one of these. It has numbers on both axes.
You use equipment to get these. They are written in numbers and units.
You are doing one of these when you collect information or evidence to help you answer a scientific question.
Changing one variable and keeping all others the same is a ...
Saying why you think something happened is suggesting an ...
Jenny said 'I think the hotter water will make the sugar dissolve faster'. She was making a ...
You get this when you get results from your investigation.
Things that you change, measure or keep the same when you are doing an investigation are ...

Splat
Word List
Words we use when we are investigating

Axis
Table
Observations
Conclusion
Bar chart
Equipment
Plan
Line Graph
Measurements
Investigation
Fair Test
Explanation
Prediction
Evidence
Variables

Splat Bingo Card 1

Axis	Table	Measurements
Investigations	Observations	Fair Test
Conclusion	Explanation	Bar Chart

Splat Bingo Card 2

Prediction	Equipment	Evidence
Plan	Variables	Line Graph
Axis	Measurements	Table

Splat Bingo Card 3

Investigations	Observations	Fair test
Plan	Evidence	Conclusion
Variables	Line graph	Axis

Splat Bingo Card 4

Measurements	Table	Investigation
Plan	Variables	Line Graph
Prediction	Equipment	Bar Chart

Splat Bingo Card 5

Equipment	Evidence	Plan
Fair test	Conclusion	Explanation
Variables	Prediction	Axis

Splat Bingo Card 6

Evidence	Plan	Measurements
Table	Fair test	Conclusion
Variables	Equipment	Observations

Conclusion

Bar Chart

Equipment

Axis

Table

Observations

Plan

Line Graph

Measurements

Investigation

Explanation

Prediction

Fair Test

Evidence

Variables

Evaluating

Blooper

Evaluating

Blooper

WHAT IS IT?

This is a quick and simple game that helps children look critically at investigations in an entertaining manner. Not only does it help them to evaluate their investigations but it can also help future planning too. Children are given a copy of a report of an investigation that has several errors in it. As you read through the report they have to respond by jumping up and shouting 'Blooper' or releasing a balloon each time they spot an error.

You can take any plan or report and introduce deliberate mistakes to play this game. Alternatively, you could take samples of children's work and use this activity as a way to review investigations. The example shows how you might do this.

WHY IS IT IMPORTANT

Evaluation is an important part of science enquiry. If they learn the importance of evaluation it will also help them to be better at planning investigations.

> Children need to realise that, even though an investigation may have progressed well, they may still be able to find ways in which they could improve the process. This will also help them to decide whether their results are reliable.

> Learning how to spot the kind of errors that can be made will help them when they are planning future investigations.

RESOURCES
Available in the book and on CD

GROWING POTATOES REPORT
(Version 1 - teacher and 1 per group)

P103

YOU WILL ALSO NEED
Wipe boards and pens. Balloons and balloon blowers (optional)

How to play Blooper

Version 1 – Whole class

- Give each group copies of the report (p103). Give them time to discuss the errors.

- Read out the report a section at a time.

- Allow a minute for them to discuss and possibly make notes on a wipe board.

- Then say "go". If they think there is an error they either stand up and shout "Blooper" or could release a blown up balloon (lots of fun but you need to know the class well to avoid chaos).

- Get children to justify their ideas.

- Gain 1 point for a correct answer and lose 1 for an incorrect answer.

- Repeat with other sections of the report.

Version 2 - CD & Whiteboard

Using the CD allows you to use whiteboard software to highlight different sections of text.

Blooper (Version 1)

1 HAND OUT THE REPORT.

2 READ OUT THE REPORT A SECTION AT A TIME.

3 ALLOW A MINUTE'S DISCUSSION.

4 SAY "GO".

GO

5 IF CHILDREN THINK THERE IS AN ERROR THEY SHOUT "BLOOPER".

BLOOPER

6 GET CHILDREN TO JUSTIFY THEIR IDEAS.

Background notes

This is a copy of a report of an investigation with *possible answers* (children may be able to justify why they have come up with a different answer).

GROWING POTATOES

1 We want to grow potatoes in our school garden. We did an investigation to find out what helps them to grow well. We wanted to use 60 potatoes but only had 50. We decided to cut 10 of the bigger potatoes in half. Now we had 60 potatoes for our test!

(Blooper – potatoes should be whole, unless cutting the potatoes in half to test if this makes a difference).

2 We dug three trenches to plant the potatoes.

* The first trench was 10 cms deep
* The next trench was 20 cms deep
* The last trench was 30 cms deep

(Not a blooper - at this stage depth could be the factor being investigated)

3 We put potatoes in each trench.

* We put 10 potatoes in the first trench
* We put 20 potatoes in the next trench
* We put 30 potatoes in the last trench

(Blooper – numbers should be the same if depth is different. NB could change the number of potatoes if the depth is kept the same).

4 We thought that fertiliser might make a difference.

* We added a bit of fertiliser to the first trench
* We added a bit more to the next trench
* We added a lot to the last trench

(Blooper - don't know accurately how much is used).

5 It took several weeks before the potatoes grew. We gave all the potatoes enough time to grow and then dug them out of the ground.

(Not a blooper).

6 It was hard work digging up the potatoes in the 30 cms trench, and the potatoes were difficult to find as well, so we left some of them in the ground.

(Blooper – Need to make sure that all the potatoes have been dug up).

7 We weighed all the potatoes that we had and put the results in a table. We made sure that we had labelled each axis. The highest column showed the best way to grow potatoes.

(Blooper – Tables don't have axes or columns).

Growing Potatoes

We want to grow potatoes in our school garden. We did an investigation to find out what helps them to grow well. We wanted to use 60 potatoes for our test but only had 50, so we decided to cut 10 of the bigger potatoes in half. Now we had 60 potatoes for our test!

We dug three trenches to plant the potatoes:

- The first trench was 10 cms deep
- The next trench was 20 cms deep
- The last trench was 30 cms deep

We put potatoes in each trench:

- We put 10 potatoes in the first trench
- We put 20 potatoes in the next trench
- We put 30 potatoes in the last trench

We thought that fertiliser might make a difference:

- We added a bit of fertiliser to the first trench
- We added a bit more to the next trench
- We added a lot to the last trench

It took several weeks before the potatoes grew. We gave all the potatoes enough time to grow and then dug them out of the ground.

It was hard work digging up the potatoes in the 30 cms trench, and the potatoes were difficult to find as well, so we left some of them in the ground.

We weighed all the potatoes that we had and put the results in a table. We made sure that we had labelled each axis. The highest column showed the best way to grow potatoes.

Enquiry
Overview

Sort It

Enquiry Overview

Sort It

WHAT IS IT?

In this game children are given a series of statements. They are asked to consider their response to the statements either True, False or It depends. The statements are chosen to challenge their overall understanding of the various aspects of scientific enquiry and the relationships between them. The teacher calls out one of the statements. The children are then given a set time to make their mind up about the statement. The teacher shouts "SORT" and the children indicate their choices. Any differences can then be discussed. The process is then repeated for the other statements.

While the other activities in the book are intended to look at specific skills, this activity covers a range of aspects of scientific enquiry. It can be used to summarise learning and to challenge ideas after the children have completed the other games. Some of the statements might also be used at other times depending on your objectives.

WHY IS IT IMPORTANT?

Although children will have considered a wide range of ideas in the previous games it is possible that some misconceptions may remain.

❯ It is helpful to give children time to explore these misconceptions together and to give you, and them, a further opportunity to develop understanding in these areas.

These might relate to:
- specific aspects of enquiry
- the nature of enquiry
- the relationship between various aspects.

❯ Despite spending time carrying out various kinds of enquiry, children can still believe that scientific enquiry is only about doing investigations, rather than recognising a wide range of ways of responding to scientific questions.

RESOURCES
Available in the book and on CD

TRUE FALSE STATEMENTS (Version 1 and 2 - teacher, Version 3 - per group)	P112

LABELS (Version 1 - teacher, Version 2 - children (optional))	P113

YOU WILL ALSO NEED
Wipe boards, pens and cloths (Version 1)
Post-its or coloured cards - (Version 2 - 1 of each of three colours per child.)

How to play Sort It

Version 1 – Whole class

- Give each child three different coloured Post-its, for example red (false), green (true) and yellow (it depends). Alternatively give them traffic light cards or copies of the three 'Labels' (p113).

- Call out one of the 'True False Statements' (p112).

- Give children a set amount of time to discuss in pairs or small groups what they think. Then individually they choose the appropriate Post-it, traffic light or card.

- On the shout of "One, two, three, sort" they stick their Post-it on their forehead or hold up their card to find everyone else who thinks the same.

- Count the numbers in each group and discuss the differences.

- Repeat for other statements.

Version 2– Whole class

- Put the Label cards (p113) in different areas of the classroom. Each group then selects a runner.

- Call out one of the 'True False statements' (p112).

- Give children a set amount of time to discuss their response. Is it true, false or does the answer depend on something? If possible ask the children to write the reason for their choice on a wipe board.

- Count down from three and shout "SORT". The runners run with their wipe board to the appropriate label.

- Justifications for their ideas can be shared and differences discussed.

- Repeat for other statements.

Version 3– Group

- Give children the True False statements (p112) to discuss in groups.

- Groups then split (jigsawing) to find out other people's views. They return to their original groups to discuss their ideas and identify disagreements.

Version 4– CD & Whiteboard

- Open 'Sort It' on the CD. You will find a True False table. Use the whiteboard pen to record the totals. This can be used with any of the versions above.

Sort It (Version 1)

1 GIVE EACH CHILD THREE DIFFERENT POST-IT NOTES.

2 CALL OUT ONE OF THE STATEMENTS.

3 CHILDREN DISCUSS WHETHER IT IS TRUE, FALSE OR IT DEPENDS.

4 CALL OUT ONE, TWO, THREE, SORT!

5 CHILDREN PUT ONE POST-IT ON THEIR FOREHEAD AND FIND OTHERS WITH THE SAME ONE.

6 CHILDREN SHARE IDEAS.

Background Notes

Here are the statements with possible answers. Some children may be able to justify why another answer is appropriate.

STATEMENTS	TRUE OR FALSE	ANSWERS
When you investigate you always have to do a fair test.	F	There are several ways to investigate, such as timed observation, which do not involve a fair test.
There is only one way of finding out the answer to scientific questions.	F	There are many ways of finding answers, such as observing, reading books, speaking to an expert, visiting a science centre, etc.
If you are observing something you are carrying out a scientific enquiry.	F or it depends	It depends on what you are observing. Observing something is one way to find the answer to a scientific problem, such as how does a tadpole change as it grows? But if you are observing someone drawing a picture, that is not really a science enquiry.
Planning makes sure you get the right answer.	F	You might make a plan but it could be the wrong plan for what you need to find out. Or you might make a plan and then ignore it. Planning can help you to think ahead and investigate more carefully.
You will not find out the answer to a question unless you do a plan.	F	Lots of questions can be answered without doing a plan. You might not do a plan if you wanted to find out how far it is to the moon or to find out which flowers are growing in the playground.
Planning can help you to decide the best way to do something.	T or it depends	It can help you to think more carefully about what you are going to do, but it doesn't guarantee that it will be the best way.
You have to repeat measurements for a test to be fair.	F	Repeating measurement is not about fairness. It is about getting reliable results.

STATEMENTS	TRUE OR FALSE	ANSWERS
It is usually best to explore your ideas first to find out what questions you want to answer.	T or it depends	Generally it is better to explore, even if very briefly, before you try to do something a bit more systematically. For example it is useful to briefly explore the way shoes slide down a ramp and how to change the speed of sliding before deciding on the best way to investigate sliding more systematically. This will raise questions about the sliding shoes and help to suggest some ways of testing the shoes. Sometimes the question is very clear because of previous experience.
Some questions cannot be answered by doing practical activity.	T	Practical activity is only one of a range of ways of answering scientific questions.
If you do not do a practical activity then it is not a scientific enquiry.	F	Practical activity is only one of a range of ways of answering scientific questions.
You should always put your results in a graph.	F	Some results will not go in a graph, for example if you have been observing.
Tables and graphs help you to understand your results.	T or it depends	It depends on the information you have and how well you draw the graphs etc. A well structured graph, that shows your results clearly, can help you to see patterns and compare data easily.
It is only a scientific enquiry if you use measuring equipment.	F	For example, getting data off the internet does not involve measuring equipment.
In a fair test you only change one thing at a time.	T	If you change more than one thing you will not know what makes a difference to your results.
In a fair test you only keep one thing the same.	F	You need to identify all the variables that must not change and there may be more than one.

Sort It
True False Statements

Discuss these statements and decide whether they are true, false or it depends.

When you have finished, talk to other people and see what they think.

STATEMENTS	TRUE	FALSE	IT DEPENDS
When you investigate you always have to do a fair test.			
There is only one way of finding out the answer to scientific questions.			
If you are observing something you are carrying out a scientific enquiry.			
Planning makes sure you get the right answer.			
You will not find out the answer to a question unless you do a plan.			
Planning can help you to decide the best way to do something.			
It is usually best to explore your ideas first to find out what questions you want to answer.			
Some questions cannot be answered by doing practical activity.			
If you do not do a practical activity then it is not a scientific enquiry.			
You should always put your results in a graph.			
Tables and graphs help you to understand your results.			
It is only a scientific enquiry if you use measuring equipment.			
You have to repeat measurements for a test to be fair.			
In a fair test you only change one thing at a time.			
In a fair test you only keep one thing the same.			

Sort It
Labels

Enlarge to A3

True

False

It depends